Geography Today

for ages 8–9

Andrew Brodie ✓

Published 2008 by A&C Black Publishers Limited
38 Soho Square, London W1D 3HB
www.acblack.com

ISBN 9781408104606

Copyright © A&C Black Publishers Limited

Written by Andrew Brodie and Judy Richardson
Illustration by Mike Phillips/Beehive Illustration
Maps by Tony Randall
Photographs by Andrew Brodie and Judy Richardson
Page layout by Bob Vickers

The writers gratefully acknowledge the co-operation of Viridor Management Ltd and of the photographers who have provided photographs for use in this book and accompanying CD-ROM.

A CIP record for this publication is available from the British Library.

Printed by Martin's the Printers, Berwick-upon-Tweed

This book is produced using paper that is made from wood grown in managed, sustainable forests. It is natural, renewable and recyclable. The logging and manufacturing processes conform to the environmental regulations of the country of origin.

To see our full range of titles visit **www.acblack.com**

CONTENTS

INTRODUCTION

The *Geography Today* series provides ample opportunities to make geography the most exciting subject on the curriculum. Based on the demands of the National Curriculum, the contents of the books reflect the need to put fun and enjoyment back into geography by ensuring that people and places are at the heart of the subject.

Never have we been more aware of global issues. Geography provides the key to helping children understand the world, its diverse environments and the roles and impacts that people create. Throughout the *Geography Today* series, children will develop their awareness of the world while building an enthusiasm for the subject of geography. At Year 4 they will consider the suitability of particular areas for settlements and will look at clues provided by place names throughout the United Kingdom; they will study India as a country that contrasts with the UK; and they will learn about how we dispose of our waste products and the uses that can be made of them.

Each book in the series consists of differentiated worksheets of fun classroom activities and fieldwork exercises. The accompanying CD-ROM contains copies of all worksheets in PDF format, together with photographs and maps to display on the whiteboard, offering many possibilities for discussion and interaction.

Much of the work should be completed as speaking, listening and visual activities. Maps and photographs to display on the whiteboard will offer many possibilities for discussion and interaction. In particular, pupils will be encouraged to 'offer reasons and evidence for their views, considering alternative opinions' and to 'respond appropriately to the contributions of others in the light of differing viewpoints' (Literacy Framework Year Four Speaking) and to 'listen to a speaker, make notes on the talk and use notes to develop a role-play' (Literacy Framework Year Four Listening).

QCA guidance for geography suggests the possible use of four units specifically for Year Four and other units for more than one age-group:

- Improving the environment
- Village settlers
- A village in India
- How and where do we spend our time?
- What's in the news? (Y3–Y6)
- Connecting ourselves to the world (Y3–Y6)
- How can we improve the area we can see from our window? (Y3–Y4)
- Passport to the world (Y1–Y6)
- Geography and numbers (Y1–Y6)

Geography Today provides support for schools following the QCA guidance as the resources can be slotted in to current teaching programmes. However some schools may prefer to use our materials independently of the QCA guidance, confident in the knowledge that they are meeting the requirements of the National Curriculum.

The National Curriculum for Key Stage Two divides geography into seven programmes of study:

1. Geographical enquiry and skills 1, which considers asking geographical questions; collecting and recording evidence; analysing evidence and drawing conclusions; identifying and explaining different views that people, including themselves, hold about topical geographical issues; communicating in ways appropriate to the task and audience.

2. Geographical enquiry and skills 2, which includes using geographical vocabulary; using fieldwork techniques and instruments; using globes, maps and plans; using secondary sources of information, including aerial photographs; drawing plans and maps at a range of scales; using ICT to help in geographical investigations; using decision-making skills.

3. Knowledge and understanding of places, including identifying and describing what places are like; the locations of places and environments they study and other significant places and environments; describing where places are; explaining why places are like they are; identifying how and why places change and how they may change in the future; describing and explaining how and why places are similar to and different from other places in the same country and elsewhere in the world.

4. Knowledge and understanding of patterns and processes, including recognising and explaining patterns made by individual physical and human features in the environment; recognising some physical and human processes and explaining how these can cause changes in places and environments.

5. Knowledge and understanding of environmental change and sustainable development, including recognising how people can improve the environment or damage it, and how decisions about places and environments affect the future quality of people's lives; recognising how and why people may seek to manage environments sustainably, and to identify opportunities for their own involvement.

6. Breadth of study through the study of two localities, one in the United Kingdom and one in a country that is less economically developed, and three themes:
   - water and its effects on landscapes and people, including the physical features of rivers or coasts, and the processes of erosion and deposition that affect them;
   - how settlements differ and change, including why they differ in size and character, and an issue arising from changes in land use;
   - an environmental issue, caused by change in an environment, and attempts to manage the environment sustainably.

7. Breadth of study – studying at a range of scales, local, regional and national; studying a range of places and environments in different parts of the world, including the UK and the EU; carrying out fieldwork investigations outside the classroom.

Places and environments listed in the National Curriculum as required for locational knowledge:

British Isles:
The two largest islands of the British Isles: Great Britain, Ireland.
The two countries: United Kingdom, the Republic of Ireland.
Capitals: Belfast, Cardiff, Dublin, Edinburgh, London.
Mountain areas: Cambrians, Grampians, Lake District, Pennines.
Longest rivers in UK: Severn, Thames, Trent.
Seas around UK: English Channel, Irish Sea, North Sea.

Europe:
Three EU countries with highest populations and their capitals: France, Germany, Italy; Paris, Berlin, Rome.
Three EU countries with largest areas and their capitals: France, Spain, Sweden; Paris, Madrid, Stockholm.
Largest mountain range: Alps
Longest river in countries listed above: Rhine
Largest seas: Mediterranean, North Sea.

World:
Continents: Africa, Asia, Europe, North America, Oceania, South America, Antarctica.
Largest city in each continent: Lagos, Tokyo, Paris, New York, Sydney, Sao Paulo.
Six countries with highest populations: Brazil, China, India, Indonesia, Russia, USA.
Six countries with largest areas: Australia, Brazil, Canada, China, Russia, USA.
Areas of family origin of the main minority ethnic groups in UK: Bangladesh, Caribbean, India, Pakistan, Republic of Ireland.
Largest mountain ranges on basis of height and extent: Andes, Himalayas, Rocky Mountains.
Three longest rivers: Amazon, Mississippi, Nile.
Largest desert: Sahara.
Oceans: Arctic, Atlantic, Indian, Pacific.
Canals linking seas/oceans: Panama, Suez.
North Pole, South Pole, Equator, Tropics, Prime Meridian.

Geography offers a multitude of opportunities for cross-curricular work. *Geography Today* gives a range of experiences in the following areas:

- Speaking and Listening, when considering all the worksheets, photographs and presentations.

- Reading, when sharing information on paper and on screen.

- Writing, when responding to questions and when making statements.

- Number, when counting people or things in surveys, when counting houses, shops, etc.

- Shape and DT, when constructing models.

- Art and Science, when making close observations in fieldwork.

- Religious Education, when sensing the awe and wonder of the world.

- ICT, when working interactively.

- History, when considering the local area and the changes that are taking place.

Geography Today 8–9

The book is divided into five units. Each unit contains worksheets that are suitable for all pupils and some have differentiated worksheets that are targeted at **three different levels**:

 sheets marked with a cat are the least demanding,

 sheets marked with a dog are suitable for most pupils,

 sheets marked with a rabbit are more difficult.

You may wish to use all three worksheets with some pupils, but to use just one or two for others. Key vocabulary used in a unit is provided at the end of each unit. Where relevant, a unit will have an accompanying CD-ROM presentation, providing a focus for discussion and serving as an introduction to the worksheets. Where individual worksheets are linked to the CD-ROM this symbol will be displayed in the teachers' notes.

Unit 1: What a load of rubbish

This unit concerns the problem of disposing of waste products: paper, waste food, plastic bottles, garden waste, glass and other packaging. What happens to it after we have thrown it out and what use can be made of it? As this is such an important current issue the unit features an extended CD-ROM presentation as well as appropriate worksheets. The first section of the CD-ROM presentation encourages the children to discuss a wide variety of waste products, all of which will be familiar to them. The next section looks at what happens to much of the rubbish after it is discarded. The third section shows the use of recycled glass as a substitute for sand in the production of concrete blocks.

Unit 2: Settlements and Counties

This unit introduces pupils to considering why people in the past settled where they did and how place names may have originated. This work provides opportunities for links to history through the study of invaders and settlers as well as work on how places have developed and changed during the more recent past. The work on counties introduces pupils to the larger area in which they live and how this fits into our country.

Unit 3: India

This unit looks at aspects of life in an economically developing country in another part of the world. In this work pupils will gain an understanding of some aspects of life in India. Pupils are shown a map of India and asked to identify particular towns and cities. There is an accompanying CD-ROM presentation about India. When looking at the photographs pupils should be encouraged to notice the details that help to inform them about ways of life.

Unit 4: Making a model to view from above

This unit provides an exciting opportunity for creative cross-curricular work covering areas of the curriculum such as Design Technology, Art and Design, Mathematics, English and Geography. The main task is to create a model of a settlement. The children are encouraged to think about the types of buildings that could be included in their settlement. They gather data and interpret it then use it to make decisions about the buildings. The children are provided with a range of nets of common shapes (Mathematics Framework Year 4: Visualise 3-D objects from 2-D drawings; make nets of common solids) from which they can create a variety of different sized buildings. More able pupils will be able to 'scale up' the nets to create their own nets on thin card so that they can make larger buildings. Ideally a board should be used for creating the scene on which the models can be placed. Pupils could draw roads, rivers or other features on to the board before positioning the buildings – in this way they will see how physical and human features affect the design of a settlement. Once the model is complete the children can use digital cameras to take photographs from 'ground level', above or oblique views. They can use these photographs to assist them in making maps of their settlement. The work could be extended into creative writing in which the pupils consider the people who might live and work in their settlement, i.e. using settings and characterisation to engage readers' interests (Literacy Framework Year 4: Creating and shaping texts).

Unit 5: Maps

This unit includes an interactive CD-ROM presentation on recognising the continents. It would be helpful if the pupils could have access to a world atlas while discussing the presentation. Three resource maps are also provided.

RECORD SHEET

Name _____

National Curriculum Level 1

I can show my knowledge in studies at a local scale. ☐

I can show my skills in studies at a local scale. ☐

I can show my understanding in studies at a local scale. ☐

I can recognise and make observations about physical features of localities. ☐

I can recognise and make observations about human features of localities. ☐

I can express my views on features of the environment of a locality. ☐

I can use resources that are given to me, and my own observations, to ask questions about places and environments. ☐

I can use resources that are given to me, and my own observations, to respond to questions about places and environments. ☐

National Curriculum Level 2

I can show my knowledge in studies at a local scale. ☐

I can show my skills in studies at a local scale. ☐

I can show my understanding in studies at a local scale. ☐

I can describe physical features of places. ☐

I can recognise and make observations about physical features that give places their character. ☐

I can describe human features of places. ☐

I can recognise and make observations about human features that give places their character. ☐

I can show an awareness of places beyond my own locality. ☐

I can express my views on features of the environment of a locality. ☐

I can recognise how people affect the environment of a locality. ☐

I can carry out simple tasks and select information using resources that are given to me. ☐

I can use this information and my own observations to help me ask and respond to questions about places and environments. ☐

I am beginning to use appropriate geographical vocabulary. ☐

National Curriculum Level 3

I can show my knowledge in studies at a local scale. ☐

I can show my skills in studies at a local scale. ☐

I can show my understanding in studies at a local scale. ☐

I can describe and compare physical features of different localities and offer explanations for the location of some of those features. ☐

I can describe and compare human features of different localities and offer explanations for the location of some of those features. ☐

I am aware that different places may have both similar and different characteristics. ☐

I offer reasons for some of my observations and for my views and judgements about places and environments. ☐

I recognise how people seek to improve and sustain environments. ☐

I can use skills and sources of evidence to respond to a range of geographical questions. ☐

I am beginning to use appropriate vocabulary to communicate my findings. ☐

Andrew Brodie: Geography Today 8–9 © A & C Black 2008

WHAT A LOAD OF RUBBISH!

Contents

This unit focuses on the problem of disposing of waste products: paper, waste food, plastic bottles, garden waste, glass and other packaging. Questions are posed such as 'What happens to rubbish after we have thrown it out and what use can be made of it?' As this is such an important current issue the unit features an extended CD-ROM presentation as well as accompanying worksheets. The first part of the presentation ('What gets thrown away?') encourages children to discuss a wide variety of waste products, all of which they will be familiar with. They are asked to consider who has thrown the articles away and why and what might happen to them next. The next part ('What happens to the rubbish?') looks at what happens to much of the rubbish after it is has been discarded. The problems of landfill are considered and the idea that the waste material and its by-product, methane, can be used to produce energy. A traditional form of recycling is shown, that of making compost from garden waste and food waste. The third part of the presentation ('Making new from old') shows the use of recycled glass as a substitute for sand in the production of concrete blocks.

This unit features:
- CD-ROM: WHAT A LOAD OF RUBBISH 1–21
  - What gets thrown away? (1–9)
  - What happens to the rubbish? (10–15)
  - Making new from old (16–21)
- Worksheets 1–6
- Vocabulary sheets 1–2

Learning objectives

- asking geographical questions
- collecting and recording evidence
- using appropriate geographical vocabulary
- using secondary sources of information
- using ICT to help in geographical investigations
- decision-making skills
- recognising physical and human features in the environment
- recognising some physical and human processes and explaining how these can cause changes in places and environments
- recognising how people can improve the environment or damage it, and how decisions about places and environments affect the future quality of people's lives
- recognising how and why people may seek to manage environments sustainably
- studying an environmental issue

The worksheets

Worksheets 1–3: What gets thrown away?   Worksheets 4–6: What happens to the rubbish?

The vocabulary sheets

The vocabulary sheets include specific geographical vocabulary as well as words that will be useful to pupils working on the activities. The sheets can be photocopied and made into flashcards which can be used for both geography and literacy. There are extra blank flashcards for you to add your own useful words.

Further research

The unit can be greatly extended by encouraging pupils to do further research on the following websites:

www.teachernet.gov.uk/teachingandlearning/library/talkingrubbish/
www.recyclezone.org.uk   www.recyclenow.com   www.slimyourbinatschool.co.uk
www.eco-schools.org.uk   www.recycle-more.co.uk   www.wasteonline.org.uk
www.scrib.org   www.thinkcans.net   www.britglass.org.uk

The CD-ROM

Main Menu What a load of rubbish: 1

What gets thrown away?

Discuss the photograph with the children. Hopefully they will identify the main subject as being broken glass. Ask questions such as: *Where do you think it came from? Why was it thrown away? What might happen to it next?*

Main Menu What a load of rubbish: 2

What gets thrown away?

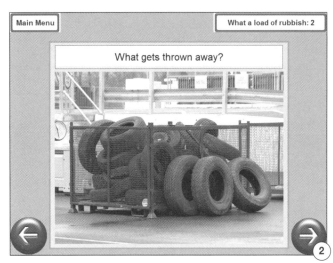

The children should notice that the tyres are from cars and vans. Explain that they have been thrown away. Ask the pupils why they might have been thrown away, and who they think might have done it.

Main Menu What a load of rubbish: 3

What gets thrown away?

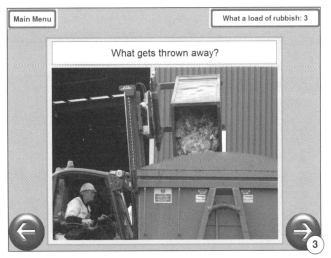

The waste products in this photograph are harder to identify. The pupils will be able to see them being tipped into a large container but what are they? Allow the pupils to make suggestions before explaining that they are waste food products. Ask them what food products get thrown away. *Apart from scraps left over from meals, millions of tons of unused food are thrown away each year. What might happen to it next?*

Main Menu What a load of rubbish: 4

What gets thrown away?

Discuss the photograph by asking the children to describe what they can see. Where do they think the man is working? What is the large object? What else is shown in the photograph?

Main Menu What a load of rubbish: 5

What gets thrown away?

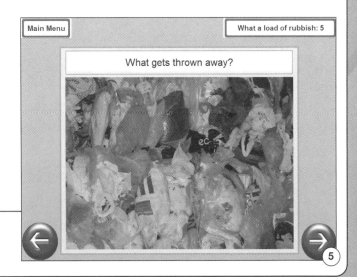

The children should be able to identify the logos and names of various retail companies on the plastic bags. Are they aware that some retailers are trying to reduce the number of plastic bags that they issue? Why?

The CD-ROM continued

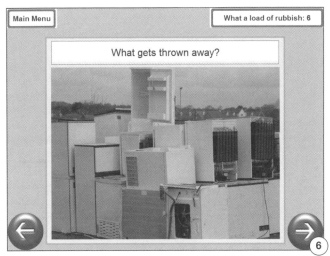

Ask the children to describe what they can see. These are obviously very large items that have been thrown away. *Why have they been thrown away? What might happen to them next?*

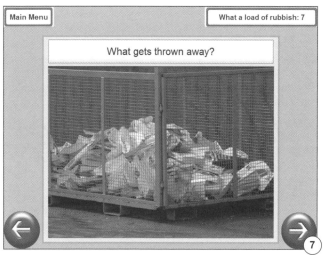

Discuss the photograph. *Why have so many copies of the yellow pages been thrown away? What could happen to them next?*

Explain that the plastic bottles are so strong that a special machine is used to make cuts in them so they can be squashed. If they were not cut, the air couldn't escape and the heavy presses wouldn't be able to flatten them. As with all of the photographs, encourage the children to think about whether it is possible to recycle the waste products. *What could happen to the plastic bottles next?*

Discuss the photograph and explain that these are bales of cans that have been flattened. *Each bale weighs a total of approximately four hundred kilograms.* An interesting extension activity would be to ask the children to find the weight of one empty can, then to use this information to find out approximately how many cans are in each bale.

The CD-ROM continued

What happens to the rubbish?

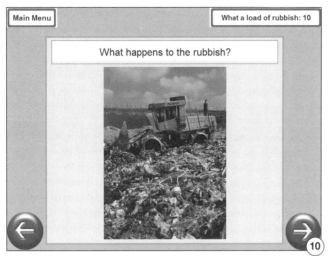

Explain that this is called a landfill site. Millions of tons of rubbish are tipped on landfill sites every year. Explain that landfill sites are often disused quarries and that the rubbish is used to fill the old quarries before they are finally covered with soil and landscaped. Ask the children why they think some people don't like having a landfill site near their homes. Would they like it near their home? *What are the unpleasant things about a landfill site? What long-term benefit could there be?*

What happens to the rubbish?

Encourage the children to realise just how big the landfill site is. *One of the problems with landfill is the release of a gas called methane from the rubbish. Eighty-five percent of the methane gas is now collected and used to produce energy – forty-seven percent of the UK's renewable energy production comes from the use of methane gas to produce electricity.*

What happens to the rubbish?

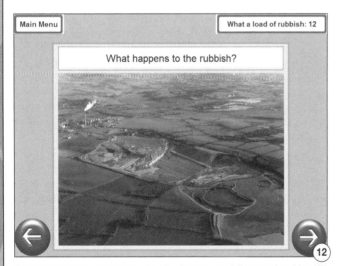

This photograph, taken from the air, shows a partially completed landfill site. Rubbish has been buried on part of the site and that is now being landscaped to restore it as part of the countryside. Can the pupils see the old quarry workings?

What happens to the rubbish?

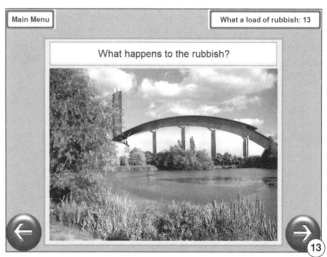

This photograph may not look as though it concerns rubbish at all. However, what the photograph shows is a 'waste to energy' plant, built on a reclaimed landfill site. Instead of the rubbish being buried, the incinerator burns it. Can the pupils identify what the problem with burning could be? Some pupils will be aware that burning produces waste gases that pollute the environment, but in the modern incinerators these gases are cleaned so that only steam is released into the atmosphere. *The cleaning process produces some polluting waste, which is then buried in landfill. However, this is only approximately seven percent of the original waste therefore overall less waste material is being buried in the ground.*

The CD-ROM continued

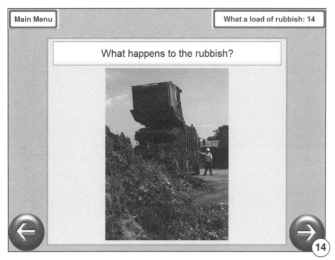

What happens to the rubbish?

This photograph shows a completely different aspect of what happens to rubbish. The compost is made from a mixture of garden waste and food waste. It represents one of the simplest forms of recycling and one that many people have done at home for generations. Discuss the photograph by asking the children to describe what they can see. Can they identify the material as compost? Do they know what the compost can be used for? Do they know what the compost is made from?

What happens to the rubbish?

This photograph gives the pupils a clearer view of the recycled compost. Explain to the children that the compost in the picture is produced from a mixture of things including, of course, garden waste but also, less obviously, food waste (food thrown away can be recycled into usable compost within just twelve weeks). The next set of slides will provide an example of recycling waste material to create new products.

Making new from old.

Explain to the pupils that in this and the following slides they are going to look at one material that can be recycled and one of the things that can be made from it. At this stage don't tell them what the material is. Ask the children if they can guess what the hands are holding. Accept answers then explain that the material consists of pieces of glass. They are not sharp as they are in the form of granules of recycled glass. Ask the pupils where the glass may have come from, then show them the next slide.

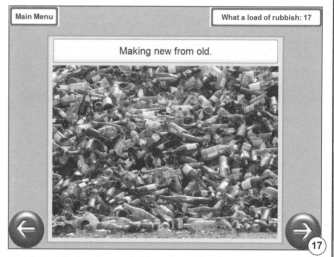

Making new from old.

Explain that the hands were holding glass. The glass was in little pieces made from waste glass, perhaps from bottles, car windows or old house windows. This photograph shows bottles that have been sent for recycling.

The CD-ROM continued

Making new from old.

Ask the children where they think this glass came from. They may be able to identify the panels of glass as broken car windscreens.

Making new from old.

Here are even more car windscreens. Thousands of windscreens are thrown away every year. Ask the children why the windscreens are thrown away – some will have experienced the windscreen of their car being shattered when hit by a stone. The children would also be correct in answering that the windscreens and other car windows could have come from old cars that have reached the end of their use.

Making new from old.

Ask the children to look again at the glass in little pieces made from waste glass. What do they think happens to the little pieces now? The next photograph will reveal the finished product.

Making new from old.

Hopefully the children will be able to identify the items as concrete blocks, used for building houses. A major constituent of concrete blocks is sand – recycled glass is used as a substitute for sand. The pupils will probably not be aware that glass is actually made from sand – using it as a substitute for sand is therefore not surprising. Explain that the manufacture of concrete blocks is just one use for recycled glass and that there are many others products that can be made such as new glass bottles, fibreglass and insulation. The children could do some research to find out other products that can be made from recycled glass, recycled plastic, recycled paper, recycled steel cans, recycled aluminium cans, etc.

What gets thrown away?

Name _____ **Date** _____

Tick the chart to show what gets thrown away in your house.
You might need to add some items of your own.

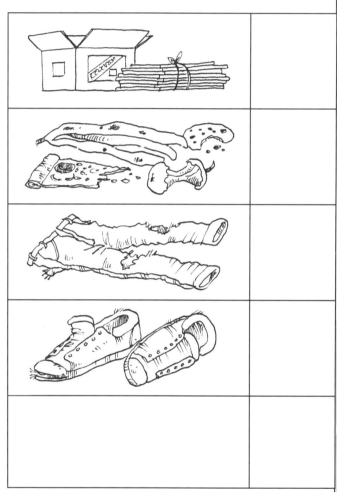

What happens to the items that are thrown away?

_____

_____

_____

_____

_____

_____

Teachers' notes Discuss the worksheet with the pupils, encouraging them to think about the rubbish that is thrown away each day or week. They may be able to add extra items to the chart: plastic yoghurt pots, cans, plastic bags, etc. For the writing exercise you could ask them some questions to prompt their writing: Is there a weekly rubbish collection? Do you have a 'wheelie bin'? Do you have recycling bins? What items go for recycling? Do any items go to charity shops?

What gets thrown away?

Name _____ **Date** _____

List the items that are thrown away in your house,
according to the materials from which they are made.

Plastic items

_____

_____

_____

Glass items

_____

_____

_____

Paper items

_____

_____

_____

Food items

_____

_____

_____

Other items

_____

_____

_____

 Teachers' notes Discuss the worksheet with the pupils, encouraging them to think about the rubbish that is thrown away each day or week. Children completing this worksheet can compare their list to the lists produced by pupils completing worksheet 3. Have both groups thought of the same items?

What gets thrown away?

Name _____ **Date** _____

Describe what happens to the items that are thrown away, according to the materials from which they are made.

Plastic items

_____

_____

_____

Glass items

_____

_____

_____

Paper items

_____

_____

_____

Food items

_____

_____

_____

Other items

_____

_____

_____

Teachers' notes Discuss the worksheet with the pupils, encouraging them to think about the rubbish that is thrown away each day or week. Prompt them with questions such as those shown on Worksheet 1 on page 15: Is there a weekly rubbish collection? Do you have a 'wheelie bin'? Do you have recycling bins? What items go for recycling? Do any items go to charity shops? Children completing this worksheet can compare their list to the lists produced by pupils doing Worksheets 1 and 2. Have all the groups thought of the same items?

Andrew Brodie: Geography Today 8–9 © A & C Black 2008

What happens to the rubbish?

Name _____ **Date** _____

┌─ **Word bank** ─┐

rubbish

waste products

landfill

digger

quarries

landscape

Now that you have seen the photographs about what happens to rubbish, try to describe what this photograph shows. These questions will give you some clues about what to write:

▶ What can you see in the picture?
▶ What is being filled?
▶ What is it being filled with?
▶ Where did the filling material come from?
▶ What will happen after the site is filled?

_____

_____

_____

_____

_____

_____

WLR 10-15 **Teachers' notes** This worksheet should be used after the children have seen the 'What happens to the rubbish?' slides. The children may need to see and discuss the slides more than once. The pupils don't need to answer all of the questions listed but these can be used to promote discussion so that they understand what they are writing about. Encourage the children to write an appropriate title for their work.

Andrew Brodie: Geography Today 8–9 © A & C Black 2008

What happens to the rubbish?

Name _____ Date _____

Word bank

rubbish

forty-seven percent

landscape

methane

energy

quarries

electricity

waste products

digger

landfill

eighty-five percent

Now that you have seen the photographs about what happens to rubbish, try to describe this photograph. These questions will give you some clues about what to write:

▶ What can you see in the photograph?

▶ What is being filled?

▶ What is it being filled with?

▶ What gas is produced?

▶ Why could that be a problem?

▶ What percentage of that gas is used to produce energy?

_____

_____

_____

_____

_____

_____

Teachers' notes This worksheet should be used after the children have seen the 'What happens to the rubbish?' slides. The children may need to see and discuss the photographs more than once. The pupils don't need to answer all of the questions listed but these can be used to promote discussion so that they understand what they are writing about. Encourage the children to write an appropriate title for their description.

Andrew Brodie: Geography Today 8–9 © A & C Black 2008

What happens to the rubbish?

Name _____   **Date** _____

The photographs that you have seen show three different ways in which waste materials are disposed of or used. Try to explain what happens to some of the many tonnes of waste that are produced in the United Kingdom each year. These questions will give you some clues about what to write:

▶ What are the three different ways in which the waste materials shown in the photographs are disposed of or used?

▶ What by-product is created at landfill sites and how is it used?

▶ Which of the waste materials do you think are easiest to deal with?

▶ Can you think of any other waste materials that are disposed of in a different way?

_____

_____

_____

_____

_____

_____

_____

_____

 Teachers' notes This worksheet should be used after the children have seen the 'What happens to the rubbish?' slides. The children may need to see and discuss the photographs more than once. The pupils don't need to answer all of the questions listed but these can be used to promote discussion so that they understand what they are writing about. Encourage the children to write an appropriate title for their description.

air	aluminium	blocks
bottle	building	cans
cardboard	clothes	community
compost	concrete	conservation
conserve	derelict	digger
energy	environment	environmental
food	glass	issues

landfill	litter	paper
plastic	pollution	quality
recycle	recycling	rubbish
rural	sorting	steel
sustain	sustainability	tyres
urban	vehicles	waste
windscreen		

SETTLEMENTS AND COUNTIES

Contents

This unit starts to explore why people in the past settled where they did and how place names may have originated. Pupils are asked to consider some specific place names. This can be further extended by looking for common elements of place names in your *local area*. Pupils should consider what might have caused the original settlements e.g. places where it was relatively easy to build fortification on land with good views and potential for defence, places where towns could develop around sources of drinking water, places where originally settlers could have arrived by water, places where it was easy to cross rivers, places with stone or wood for building, etc. This work provides opportunities for links to history and the study of invaders and settlers as well as work on how places have developed and changed during the more recent past.

The work on counties introduces pupils to the larger area in which they live and how this fits into our country. Students should be encouraged to think, speak and write using the appropriate geographical vocabulary when referring to a county or region they have visited and how this compares with the area in which they live. You may wish to investigate, as a class, the total number of counties or regions in the British Isles that pupils have visited.

This unit features:
- Worksheets 1–5
- Resource sheets 1–3

Useful resources

- Map of the United Kingdom that is detailed enough to show a large number of towns

Learning objectives

- asking geographical questions
- collecting and recording evidence
- analysing evidence and drawing conclusions
- using appropriate geographical vocabulary
- using maps and plans at a range of scales
- using secondary sources of information
- identifying and describing what places are like
- locating and describing where places are
- explaining why places are like they are
- identifying how and why places change

- describing and explaining how and why places are similar to and different from other places in the same country
- recognising how places fit within a wider geographical context and are interdependent
- recognising physical and human features in the environment
- studying how settlements differ and change
- studying a locality in the United Kingdom at a range of scales

The worksheets

Worksheet 1: Where we live
Worksheet 2: Place names in the United Kingdom
Worksheet 3: Matching places to the meanings of their names

Worksheet 4: Place names on the map
Worksheet 5: Counties and regions

The resource sheets

Resource sheet 1: Names of settlements
Resource sheet 2: Map of the British Isles

Resource sheet 3: Key to the map

Where we live

Name _____ **Date** _____

Imagine a country just like the British Isles but with no one living there. There would be no buildings, no roads, and no farms. There would be woods and forests; rivers and lakes; mountains, hills and valleys. In fact all the natural things that were in the British Isles before anyone made a home here.

Now imagine you have just arrived.
What sort of place would you choose to stay and live in?

Work with a partner to decide what features you would look for in your search for a place to live. Remember you will need to grow or gather some food, and you may want to keep animals, you would want to build a shelter and find fresh water to drink.

Write notes or draw a labelled picture of the sort of site you would choose as a place to live. Be ready to tell the rest of the class about your choices.

Teachers' notes This page is designed to encourage pupils of all abilities to engage in speaking and listening by discussing the establishment of a settlement. Some children will need extra help reading the information on the sheet and possibly in writing labels for their picture.

Andrew Brodie: Geography Today 8–9 © A & C Black 2008

Place names in the United Kingdom

Name _____ Date _____

Find at least one example of a place name in the United Kingdom that contains the word or part word shown in the left-hand column. You will need to look in an atlas or map of the British Isles.

Part word	Place name
ham	
ford	
by	
chester	
bury	
north	
south	
east	
west	
ton	
tun	
aber	
ness	
porth	
minster	
kil	
kirk	

Teachers' notes The children will need a map of the United Kingdom that is detailed enough to show a large number of towns. Alternatively, they could make use of an atlas. It would be helpful to discuss their findings with them. For each place that they find you could ask them whether it is in England, Northern Ireland, Scotland or Wales. You could ask them if they can identify which county it is in and how far away it is from your area, etc.

Matching places to the meanings of their names

Name _____   Date _____

Using Resource sheet 1 to help you, write each of the place names beside the possible correct definition.

Chester **Oxford** **Aberdeen** **Grimsby** **Birmingham** **Bury St. Edmunds** **Taunton** **Skegness** **Porthcawl** **Westminster** **Falkirk**	

	Headland, possibly lived on by a man called Skegg
	Old Roman town or fortification
	A manor or town with which St. Edmund is connected.
	Village of Boerma (now pronounced 'Birma').
	A place with a church.
	Shallow place where oxen could cross the river.
	Place to the west of the city, with a monastery.
	Village of a man called 'Grim'.
	Town at the mouth of the River Dee.
	Harbour where sea kale grows.
	Village or manor on the river Tone.

Teachers' notes Once the children have completed the table they could discuss their findings with someone who has completed the rabbit worksheet. They could share information about what each name means and where the town is located in the United Kingdom.

Place names on the map

Name _____ Date _____

Can you find where these places are on the map of the British Isles?
Write the names in the correct boxes and draw an arrow to the
correct place on the map.

Chester	**Oxford**	**Aberdeen**	**Grimsby**
Birmingham	**Bury St. Edmunds**	**Taunton**	**Skegness**
Porthcawl	**Westminster**	**Falkirk**	

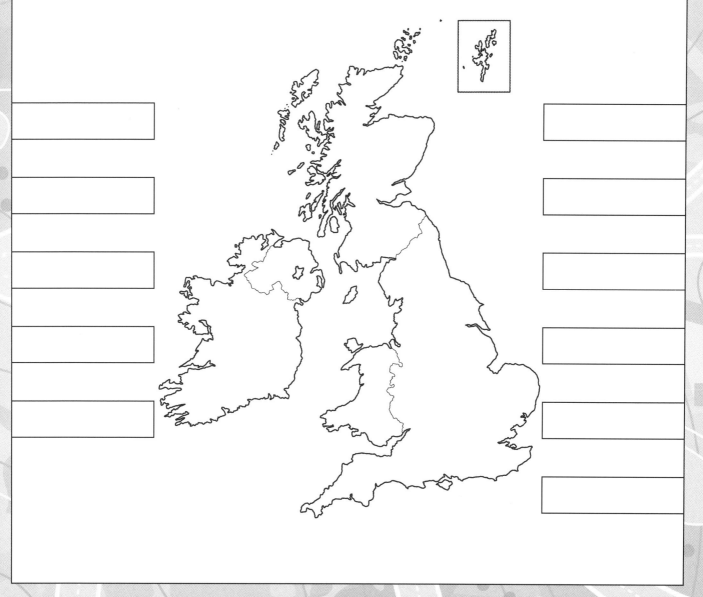

Teachers' notes To enable them to locate each town correctly the children will need to make use of a map of the United Kingdom that is detailed enough to show a large number of towns. Alternatively, they could use an atlas. Once the children have labelled the map they could discuss their work with someone who has completed the dog worksheet. They could share information regarding what each name means and where the town is located in the United Kingdom.

Andrew Brodie: Geography Today 8–9 © A & C Black 2008

Counties and regions

Name _____ **Date** _____

The British Isles is divided into areas called 'counties' in England, Wales and Ireland and 'regions' in Scotland. Each of these areas has a main town or city with local government offices.

The map of the British Isles on Resource sheet 2 has all the counties and regions marked on it. It would be difficult to write the names of each county on a map of this size, so each county has been given a number instead.

On Resource sheet 3 there is a list of the numbers with the correct county name by each number. When colours, numbers or symbols are used on a map it is called a 'key'. The map you will use has a 'number key'.

1. Look at the map to find and colour the county or region that you live in.

2. Now find each county or region that has an edge that touches your county or region. Use a different colour for each of these.

3. Look for other counties, regions or districts that you have visited. You could colour each of these.

4. Tell a partner about each of the counties you have visited. Think about:
   • Why you went there
   • How you got there
   • How long it took to get there
   • In what ways it is different from the area you live in.

5. Now write about one of the counties you have visited.

_____

_____

_____

_____

_____

Teachers' notes This page is designed to encourage pupils of all abilities to look closely at a map of the United Kingdom to understand about counties and regions. Some children will need extra help reading the information on the sheet. Pupils are asked to engage in speaking and listening by discussing counties that they have visited. The last task may not be suitable for all abilities.

Andrew Brodie: Geography Today 8–9 © A & C Black 2008

Names of settlements

Read the information below. It will help you with your worksheet.

In the past, people reached the British Isles by sea and chose suitable places to settle. They built their settlements and gave them names that often reflected the type of place or the name of the person who had first made a home there. Over the centuries, the names have gradually changed though many still give clues as to their past.

A place name ending in 'ford' tells us that the settlement came about as it was possible to cross the river there. The word 'ford' means a shallow part of a river where people and animals can cross. Place names that include words such as 'Caester, Ceaster, Chester or Caster' have been the site of old Roman forts or were old Roman towns in the past. You can see how the word has changed in spelling over the years. Place names ending in 'by' indicate that the Vikings settled there as 'by' means farm or village in the Scandinavian language used at that time.

Below are some more word parts to help you to work out what some place names meant when people first settled there.

Ham	an old English word, meaning village or homestead.
Bury	this means manor
Tun/Ton	this too means manor or village
Aber	meaning river mouth
Ness	meaning headland
Porth	harbour (names including porth are commonly found in Wales and Cornwall)
Minster	this indicates a church or monastery
Kil/Kirk	these both mean church

Some place names are very easy to work out as they have very obvious parts to them. Many place names include north, south, east or west whilst others have clues such as bridge, market, green, field, sand or stone. Some names have evolved since they were first thought of but are still quite easy to work out e.g. 'somer' originated as summer and 'ald' comes from old.

Andrew Brodie: Geography Today 8–9 © A & C Black 2008

Map of the British Isles

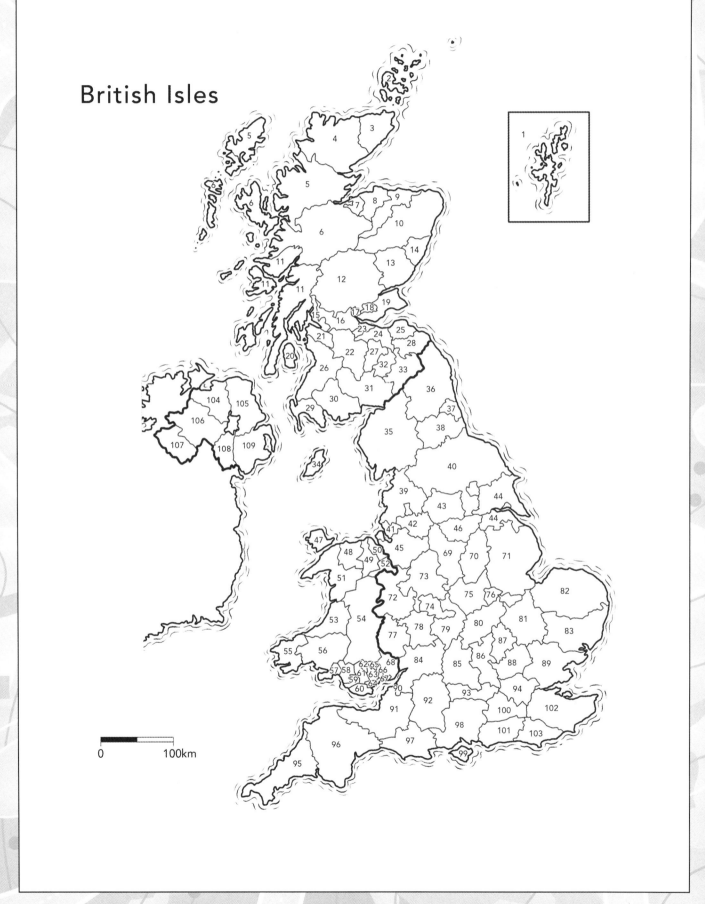

British Isles

Teachers' notes This resource sheet should be used in conjunction with worksheet 5 and resource sheet 3.

Key to the map

1 Shetland	55 Pembrokeshire
2 Orkney	56 Carmarthenshire
3 Caithness	57 Swansea
4 Sutherland	58 Neath Port Talbot
5 Ross and Cromarty	59 Bridgend
6 Inverness-shire	60 Vale of Glamorgan
7 Nairnshire	61 Rhondda Cynon Taff
8 Morayshire	62 Merthyr Tydfil
9 Baniffshire	63 Caerphilly
10 Aberdeenshire	64 Cardiff
11 Argyll	65 Blaenau Gwent
12 Perthshire	66 Torfaen
13 Angus	67 Newport
14 Kincardineshire	68 Monmouthshire
15 Dumbartonshire	69 Derbyshire
16 Stirlingshire	70 Nottinghamshire
17 Clackmannanshire	71 Lincolnshire
18 Kinross-shire	72 Shropshire
19 Fife	73 Staffordshire
20 Bute	74 Birmingham
21 Renfrewshire	75 Leicestershire
22 Lanarkshire	76 Rutland
23 West Lothian	77 Herefordshire
24 Midlothian	78 Worcestershire
25 East Lothian	79 Warwickshire
26 Ayrshire	80 Northamptonshire
27 Peebles-shire	81 Cambridgeshire
28 Berwickshire	82 Norfolk
29 Wigtownshire	83 Suffolk
30 Kirkudbrightshire	84 Gloucestershire
31 Dumfriesshire	85 Oxfordshire
32 Selkirkshire	86 Bucks
33 Roxburghshire	87 Bedfordshire
34 Isle of Man	88 Hertfordshire
35 Cumbria	89 Essex
36 Northumberland	90 Bristol
37 Tyne and Wear	91 Somerset
38 Durham	92 Wiltshire
39 Lancs	93 Berkshire
40 North Yorkshire	94 London
41 Merseyside	95 Cornwall
42 Greater Manchester	96 Devon
43 West Yorkshire	97 Dorset
44 East Yorkshire	98 Hampshire
45 Cheshire	99 Isle of Wight
46 South Yorkshire	100 Surrey
47 Isle of Anglesey	101 West Sussex
48 Conwy	102 Kent
49 Denbighshire	103 East Sussex
50 Flintshire	104 Londonderry
51 Gwynedd	105 Antrim
52 Wrexham	106 Tyrone
53 Credigion	107 Fermanagh
54 Powys	108 Armagh
	109 Down

Teachers' notes This resource sheet should be used in conjunction with worksheet 5 and resource sheet 2.

bridleway	building	city
counties	country	county
district	features	flooding
forests	fortification	government
harbour	hills	homestead
invaders	key	lakes
local	manor	monastery

Andrew Brodie: Geography Today 8–9 © A & C Black 2008

motorway	mountains	mouth
natural	offices	path
region	river	rivers
Roman	routeways	Saxon
settlement	settlers	town
valleys	Vikings	village
woods		

Andrew Brodie: Geography Today 7–8 © A & C Black 2008

INDIA

Contents

This unit looks at aspects of life in an economically developing country in another part of the world. In this unit, pupils will gain an understanding of some aspects of life in India. They will look at a map of India and try to identify particular towns and cities. It's important that pupils appreciate that in India, as in most countries, there is a mixture of urban and rural living environments. The CD-ROM features a variety of different views of India: an Indian town market; street scenes including shops and traffic; modern buildings and the makeshift shelters people build for themselves on the streets. When looking at these photographs, pupils should be encouraged to notice the details that help to inform them about how people in India lead their lives.

This unit features:
- CD-ROM: INDIA 1–15
- Worksheets 1–5
- Vocabulary sheets 1–2

Learning objectives

- asking geographical questions
- using appropriate geographical vocabulary
- using maps and plans at a range of scales
- using secondary sources of information
- identifying and describing what places are like
- locating and describing where places are
- identifying how and why places change
- describing and explaining how and why places are similar to and different from other places in the same country and elsewhere in the world

- recognising how places fit within a wider geographical context
- recognising physical and human features in the environment
- studying a locality in a country that is less economically developed
- studying a range of places and environments in different parts of the world.

Useful resources

- A photograph of a local market
- an atlas

The worksheets

Worksheet 1: World map
Worksheet 2: Map of India
Worksheet 3: India – on the road
Worksheet 4: Comparing India to the United Kingdom
Worksheet 5: Life in India and in the United Kingdom

The vocabulary sheets

The vocabulary sheets include specific geographical vocabulary as well as words that will be useful to pupils working on the activities. The sheets can be photocopied and made into flashcards which can be used for both geography and literacy. There are extra blank flashcards for you to add your own useful words.

CD-ROM

What is being sold?

Discuss the photograph with the children encouraging them to look in detail at the goods being sold in this market. They should consider why the stallholders are sitting on the ground and should realise that the shades over the stalls are largely for protection from the sun rather than rain! Explain that this is a market in India. Ask the children: *Does it look like the market in your nearest town? What's the same and what's different from your market? How are goods wrapped when they are sold in this Indian market? Why do you think some of the stalls have 'tops' over them?*

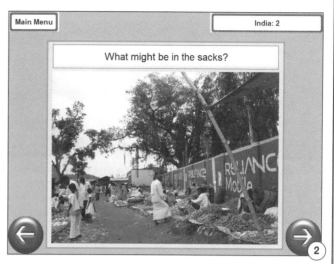

What might be in the sacks?

Explain that this is another part of the same market. It would be helpful if you were able to show pupils photographs of your local market so they can make detailed comparisons. It's important for pupils to be told that not every market in India would look exactly like this; it is a large country with a variety of styles of market. Ask the children to look at the ground in the photograph and to discuss whether it is like the ground in a market near them? What do they think might be in the sacks? Discuss whether they think it would be better to have a stall at the edge of the market or nearer the centre.

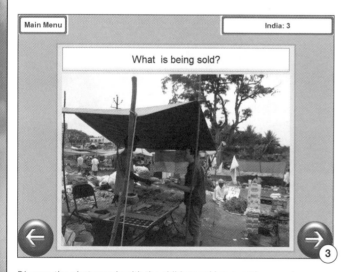

What is being sold?

Discuss the photograph with the children asking questions such as: *What do you think is being sold at this stall? Why do you think this stall has a table? Does this stall tell you anything about Indian cooking?*

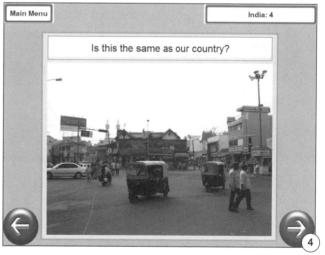

Is this the same as our country?

Look at the photograph with the children asking questions such as: *How many taxis can you see? What side of the road are they driving on? Is this the same as our country? How many shops can you see in the background?* Do you notice anything unusual about the road? Pupils should notice that the road has no markings to indicate where the vehicles should go. You may like to identify and discuss the building in the background and talk about places of worship in your local area.

CD-ROM continued

Main Menu India: 5

What sort of things are being sold in this shop?

5

When looking at these photographs pupils should see that the goods on sale reflect the needs of the community. They should notice the ice to keep food and drink cool in the hot climate. Talk about how we keep things cold and ensure that children understand that many people living in India would have electricity and therefore be able to use refrigerators. Ask questions such as: *What sort of things do you think are being sold in this shop? In what ways is the shop like a shop that you have visited?*

Main Menu India: 6

What do you think is being sold in this shop?

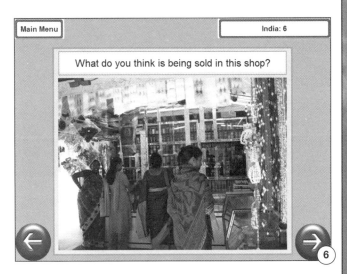

6

Discuss the photograph with the children asking questions such as: What do you think is being sold in this shop and what might it be used for?

Main Menu India: 7

What do you think this vehicle is used for?

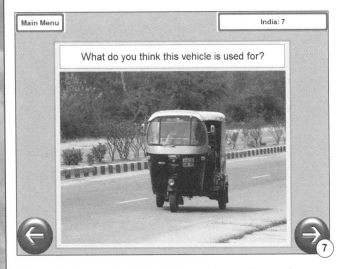

7

Discuss the photograph with the children asking questions such as: *What do you think this vehicle is used for? How many wheels does it have? What is it carrying?* The three-wheeled taxis provide an interesting talking point and pupils may notice that the photograph shows that vehicles travel on the left hand side of the road in India.

Main Menu India: 8

What can you see on top of the bus?

8

The bus to Bangalore may provoke a discussion on safety (the passenger riding on the roof rack) and climate (the windows opened wide). Ask the children questions such as: *Where do you think this bus is going? What can you see on top of the bus?*

CD-ROM continued

Main Menu
India: 9

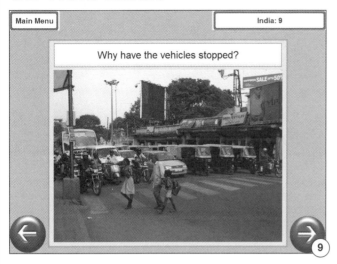

Why have the vehicles stopped?

Discuss this busy street scene with the children asking questions such as: *Why have the vehicles stopped? How many different types of vehicle are in the picture? What features are similar to our country? What features are different?*

Main Menu
India: 10

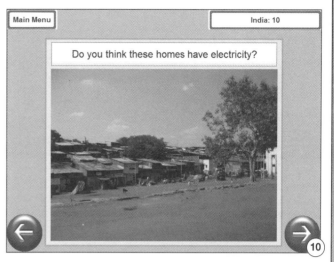

Do you think these homes have electricity?

Discuss the photograph with the children explaining that it shows a residential area. Ask questions such as: *Would you like to live in a house like the ones shown in the photograph and if not why not? Why are there no cars outside the homes? Do you think these homes have electricity?* Pupils will appreciate that the homes shown in the picture are very basic. You could discuss the difficulties of living in these small, very basic dwellings with none of the usual services your pupils are used to, (electricity, running water etc) and the effect this has on life.

Main Menu
India: 11

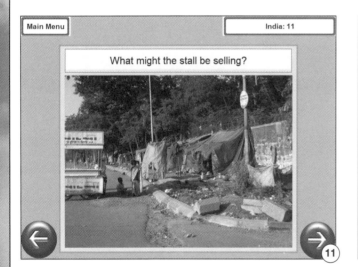

What might the stall be selling?

Ask the children what they think this photograph shows. The photograph shows even more basic living conditions than those shown in previous photographs. People here have just used any available materials to provide shelter for themselves. Pupils could speculate on what the stall in the photograph might be selling.

Main Menu
India: 12

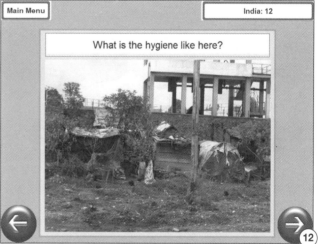

What is the hygiene like here?

Ask the pupils what this photograph tells them about life for some people in India. Hygiene in these conditions will be a major issue to consider.

CD-ROM continued

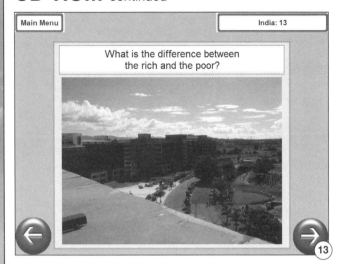

What is the difference between
the rich and the poor?

The next set of photographs will help pupils to understand that some aspects of life in India may be similar to life in a town in their local area. The first photograph shows clean modern buildings. Encourage the children to contrast this scene with the previous photographs: *You have seen photographs of some very poor homes in an Indian city. Now look at this photograph of a modern area of an Indian city. There are well-tended gardens, offices and apartment buildings and cars parked in a parking area.*

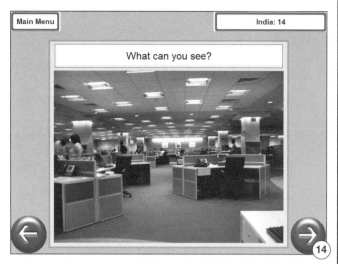

What can you see?

This photograph shows the inside of an Indian office building. People who are lucky enough to have a good education may work in a modern office building in the city. This will provide a comfortable working environment including air conditioning to keep the employees cool.

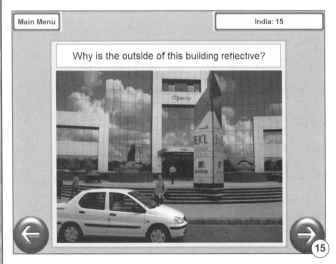

Why is the outside of this building reflective?

This photograph shows the outside of the building with a car outside. Ask the pupils why do you think the outside of it has a reflective surface? (You could give the children a clue by asking them what the climate is like in India.)

World map

Name —————————— **Date** ——————————

India is a large country. Much of India is very warm as it is much nearer to the equator than Great Britain. Find and colour in India. Now find and colour in the British Isles.

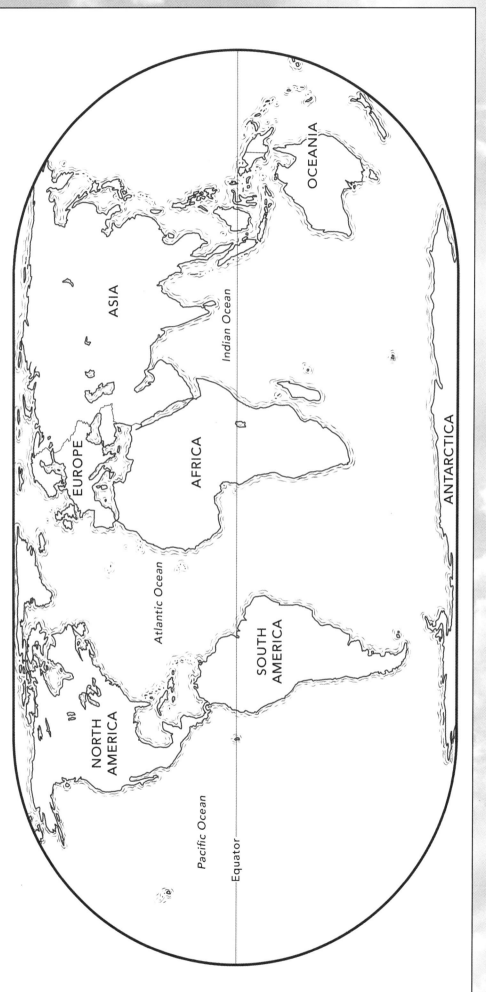

Map of India

Name _____ **Date** _____

India, like most countries, has villages, towns and cities. Some towns and cities are marked on the map. They are listed below. Use an atlas to help you to name the towns and cities on the map.

Ahmedabad	**Bhopal**	**Bangalore**	**Calcutta**
Chandigarh	**Delhi**	**Hyderabad**	**Jaipur**
Madras	**Mumbai**	**Pune**	

India – on the road

Name _____   Date _____

Look at this picture of a bus in India.

Describe two things that are different about it from the buses you see in this country.

1. _____

_____

2. _____

_____

Describe one thing that is the same as the buses you see in this country.

1. _____

_____

Write about two differences between life in India and life in the United Kingdom.

1. _____

_____

2. _____

_____

Teachers' notes Discuss the photograph with the pupils, perhaps showing them again the colour photograph on the CD-ROM. The bus to Bangalore may provoke a discussion on safety (the passenger riding on the roof rack) and climate (the windows opened wide). In completing the final task you could show pupils the complete CD-ROM presentation again or allow them to have access to it to go through at their own pace.

Comparing India to the United Kingdom

Name _____   Date _____

In the table below write a sentence or two about each aspect of life
in the two countries.

INDIA	UNITED KINGDOM
At the market	
In the street	
Keeping food cold	

Teachers' notes Discuss the worksheet with the pupils, reminding them of the CD-ROM presentation. Encourage them to find contrasts and similarities between the two countries. Help them to realise that India is much hotter than the United Kingdom and because of this people have to adapt their lifestyle.

Andrew Brodie: Geography Today 8–9 © A & C Black 2008

Life in India and the United Kingdom

Name _____ **Date** _____

Think about the photographs you have looked at. What differences have you noticed about life in India and what similarities, if any?

On a separate sheet of paper write a comparison between life in India and life in the United Kingdom. Your work should begin with a short introductory paragraph. Remember to write a paragraph for each aspect of life that you have decided to include. Your final paragraph should sum up your work.

Use the box below to spend a few minutes planning your work.

Comparing town life in United Kingdom with town life in India.

Teachers' notes This is a very demanding activity. Pupils will need reminding of the photographs that they have seen on the CD-ROM. It would be useful for them to have access to this so that they can look through the photographs at their own pace. They may need some help in deciding what aspects of life each paragraph should focus on. The final result of their work should be a well-presented piece of writing in clear paragraphs.

15

Andrew Brodie: Geography Today 8–9 © A & C Black 2008

agriculture	Ahmedabad	Asia
Bangalore	Bhopal	Calcutta
Chandigarh	city	climate
compare	comparison	continent
country	Delhi	difference
different	distance	economic
equator	Europe	Ganges

Hyderabad	**India**	**Indian**
Jaipur	**Madras**	**market**
modern	**monsoon**	**Mumbai**
Ocean	**Pune**	**shade**
similar	**similarity**	**stall**
taxi	**trade**	**tropical**
United Kingdom	**weather**	

MAKING A MODEL TO VIEW FROM ABOVE

Contents

This unit provides an exciting opportunity for creative cross-curricular work covering areas of the curriculum such as Design Technology, Art, Mathematics, English and Geography. Explain to the pupils that they are going to create a model of a settlement – the settlement could be a village but it could be part of a town or part of a city.

Worksheets 1–3 are designed to encourage the children to think about the types of buildings that could be included in their settlement. They gather data, interpret it and then use it to make decisions about their buildings. This process encourages them to consider buildings as homes, workplaces, recreational or leisure facilities, historical buildings or places of worship.

Worksheets 4–9 provide a range of nets of common shapes (Mathematics Framework Year 4: Visualise 3-D objects from 2-D drawings; make nets of common solids) from which they can create a variety of different sized buildings. The buildings could be houses, blocks of flats or offices, factories, schools, places of worship, etc, all made from individual solid shapes or solid shapes combined together. More able pupils will be able to 'scale up' the nets to create their own versions on thin card so that they can make larger buildings.

How to build the models

Photocopy several copies of each of the nets (Worksheets 4–9) onto thin card. Encourage the children to cut them out very accurately and to take care when scoring by using a sharp pencil along the edge of a ruler. The tabs should be glued then stuck into position. The more precise the pupils are with this process, the more successful their buildings will be as, once the solid shapes are constructed, they will be combined together to create different buildings e.g. the pyramid can be stuck onto the cube to create a house with a 'pointed' roof. Alternatively, the smaller triangular prism could be stuck onto the cube to make a more traditional looking house.

Ideally the models should be placed on a board where pupils could draw roads, rivers or other features before fixing the buildings in place – in this way they will see how physical and human features affect the design of a settlement. Once the model is complete the children could use digital cameras to take photographs from ground level, above or oblique views. These photographs could then be used as references for drawing maps of their settlement.

The work could be extended into creative writing in which the pupils could write about the people who might live and work in their settlement, Literacy Framework Year 4: Creating and shaping texts: 'using settings and characterisation to engage readers' interests.

If there is more than one Year 4 class in your school, each of the classes could make their own settlement then 'visit' each other's identifying similarities and differences.

This unit features:
- Worksheets 1–9
- Vocabulary sheet 1

Useful resources
- Digital camera.

Learning objectives

- asking geographical questions
- using appropriate geographical vocabulary
- collecting and recording evidence
- analysing evidence and drawing conclusions
- identifying and explaining different views that people, including themselves, hold about topical geographical issues
- using maps and plans at a range of scales
- using secondary sources of information
- drawing maps and plans at a range of scales
- decision-making skills
- identifying and describing what places are like
- explaining why places are like they are
- recognising physical and human features in the environment
- recognising some physical and human processes and explaining how these can cause changes in places and environments
- recognising how people can improve the environment or damage it, and how decisions about places and environments affect the future quality of people's lives
- studying how settlements differ and change, including why they differ in size and character

The worksheets

Worksheet 1: Planning a settlement
Worksheet 2: Gathering data (tally chart)
Worksheet 3: Gathering data (bar chart)
Worksheet 4: Net of a cube
Worksheet 5: Net of a pyramid and triangular prism
Worksheet 6: Net of a cuboid
Worksheet 7: Net of a triangular prism
Worksheet 8: Net of a cylinder
Worksheet 9: Net of a hexagonal prism

Planning a settlement

Name _____   **Date** _____

You are going to make a model of a settlement. You must consider what buildings are needed in your settlement. You may need buildings for a wide variety of purposes. Look at this key showing a range of building purposes.

Key to building use

(D) for dwellings   (S) for schools   (E) for employment

(SH) for shops   (W) for places of worship   (L) for leisure

(R) for recreation   (H) for historical buildings

Look at the list of buildings in the table below.

1. Write the correct letter next to each type of building and put a tick if you feel that buildings of this type are needed in your settlement. Some buildings may need more than one letter.
2. You may have some ideas for buildings that are not listed and you can write these in the empty boxes.

house			bungalow			flats		
school			college			factory		
farm			clothes shop			food shop		
restaurant			church			mosque		
temple			sports centre			swimming pool		
cinema			theatre			museum		
castle			offices			windmill		

Teachers' notes This worksheet is for pupils of all abilities. Discuss the word 'settlement'. This term is commonly used in both history and geography meaning an area where people first settled i.e. made their homes. Encourage the pupils to realise that every village, town or city can be considered as a settlement because people must have made the decision to establish homes there at some time in the past. Read through this worksheet with the pupils, ensuring that they understand the key – do they know what dwellings are, for example? Ask the children to complete the table individually, then gather their findings to record on the next two worksheets.

Gathering data (tally chart)

Name _____   **Date** _____

What does everybody in the class think?
Record how many people think there should
be each type of building in the settlement.
You could tally the votes for each building.

house	
bungalow	
flats	
school	
college	
factory	
farm	
clothes shop	
food shop	
restaurant	
church	
mosque	
temple	
sports centre	
swimming pool	
cinema	
theatre	
museum	
castle	
offices	
windmill	

Teachers' notes Ensure that the pupils know how to tally. This worksheet can be completed by the whole class together, taking data from the previous individually completed worksheets. Once the data has been tallied on this worksheet it can be entered on the bar chart on Worksheet 3.

Andrew Brodie: Geography Today 8–9 © A & C Black 2008

Gathering data (bar chart)

Name _____ **Date** _____

Record how many people think there should be each type of
building in the settlement by completing the bar chart.

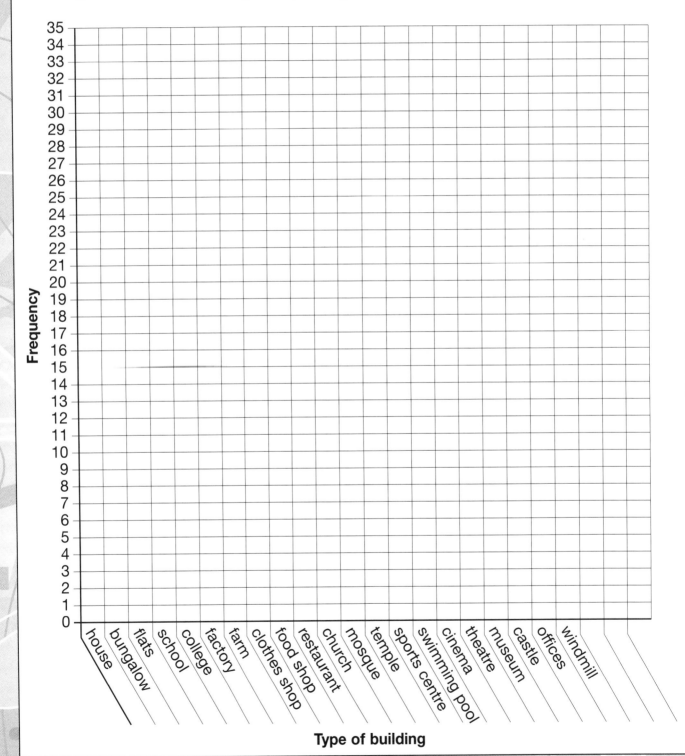

Teachers' notes Help the children to complete the bar chart, perhaps by completing the first one or two bars with them, from the data collected on Worksheet 2. Discuss the findings with the pupils and help them to make decisions about which buildings are needed for the model settlement. Encourage them to consider whether a building should not be included simply because only a few people voted for it? Can pupils make a strong case for a particular building? Once the decisions have been made the pupils can start creating the buildings from the nets provided on Worksheets 4–9.

Andrew Brodie: Geography Today 8–9 © A & C Black 2008

Net of a cube

You are going to make a model of a building. Below is the net of a cube.
You can make the cube then use it as your building or as part of your building.

1. Cut out the net then score along the dotted lines.

2. Fold it to make it into a cube.

3. Glue the tabs then press them firmly into place.

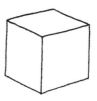

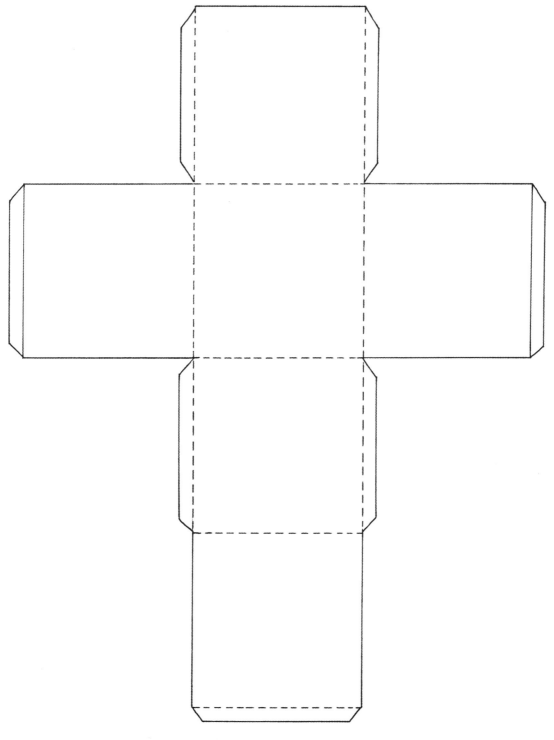

Teachers' notes Photocopy several copies of this net onto thin card. Encourage the children to cut it out very accurately and to take care when scoring by using a sharp pencil along the edge of a ruler. The tabs should be glued then stuck in position.

Andrew Brodie: Geography Today 8–9 © A & C Black 2008

Net of a pyramid and a triangular prism

You are going to make a model of a building. Below are the net of a pyramid and the net of a triangular prism. You can make the pyramid or prism then use it as the roof of your building.

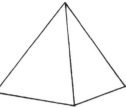

1. Cut out the net then score along the dotted lines.

2. Fold it to make it into a pyramid shape.

3. Glue the tabs then press them firmly into place.

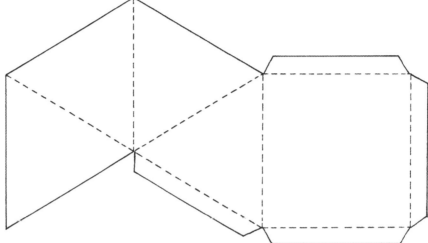

1. Cut out the net then score along the dotted lines.

2. Fold it to make it into a triangular prism.

3. Glue the tabs then press them firmly into place.

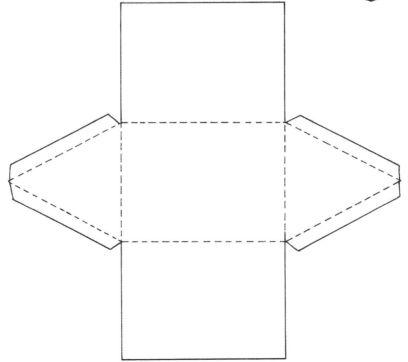

Teachers' notes Photocopy several copies of these nets onto thin card. Encourage the children to cut them out very accurately and to take care when scoring by using a sharp pencil along the edge of a ruler. The tabs should be glued then stuck in position.

Net of a cuboid

You are going to make a model of a building. Below is the net of a cuboid.
You can make the cuboid then use it as your building or as part of your building.

1. Cut out the net then score along the dotted lines.

2. Fold it to make it into a cuboid.

3. Glue the tabs then press them firmly into place.

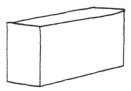

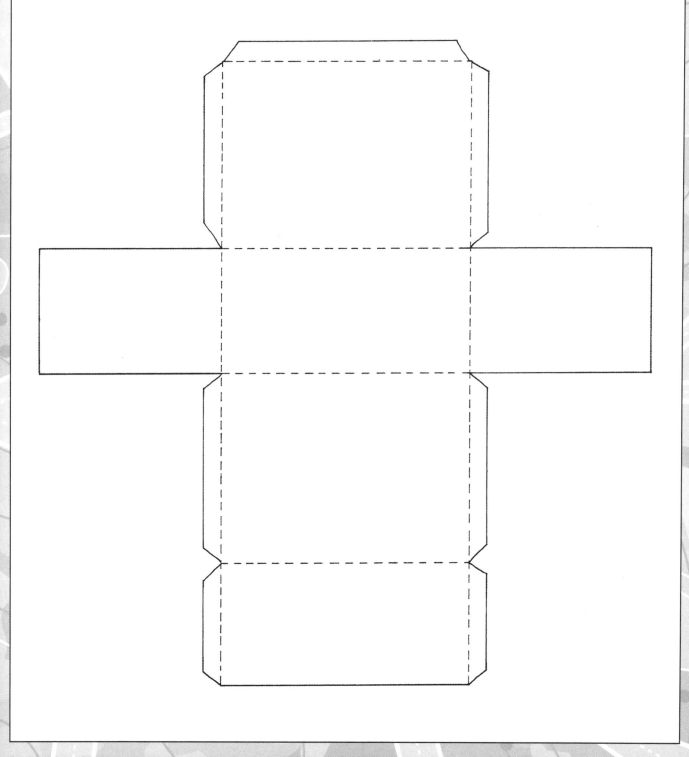

Teachers' notes Photocopy several copies of this net onto thin card. Encourage the children to cut it out very accurately and to take care when scoring by using a sharp pencil along the edge of a ruler. The tabs should be glued then stuck in position.

Net of a triangular prism

You are going to make a model of a building. Below is the net of a triangular prism. You can make the triangular prism as the roof of your building.

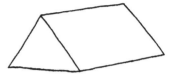

1. Cut out the net then score along the dotted lines.

2. Fold it to make it into a triangular prism.

3. Glue the tabs then press them firmly into place.

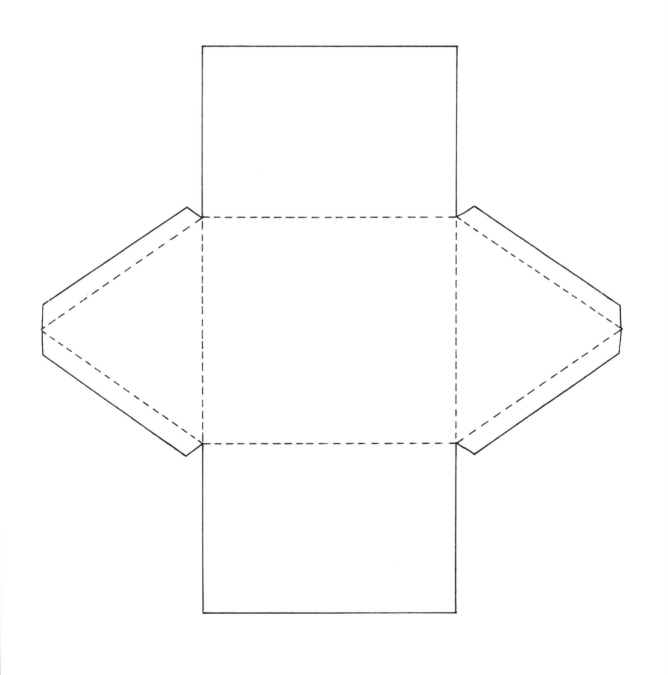

Teachers' notes Photocopy several copies of this net onto thin card. Encourage the children to cut it out very accurately and to take care when scoring by using a sharp pencil along the edge of a ruler. The tabs should be glued then stuck in position.

Net of a cylinder

You are going to make a model of a building. Below is the net of a cylinder. You can make the cylinder then use it as your building or as part of your building.

1. Cut out the net then score along the dotted lines.

2. Fold it and roll it to make it into a cylinder. You might find it easier if you roll the rectangle around another solid cylinder, such as a glue stick.

3. Glue the tabs then press them firmly into place.

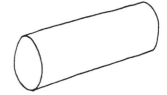

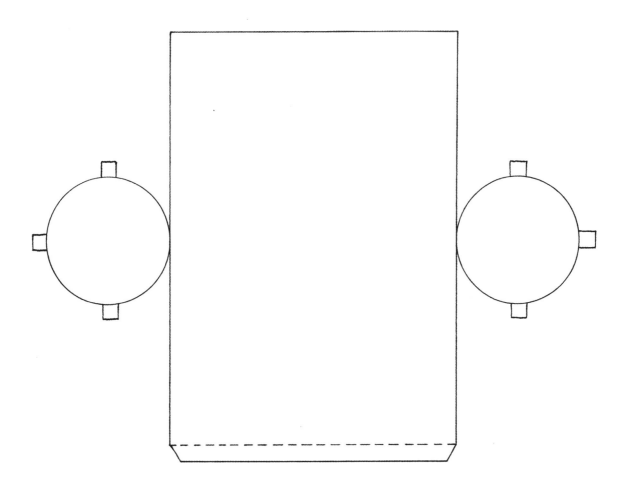

Teachers' notes Photocopy several copies of this net onto thin card. Encourage the children to cut it out very accurately and to take care when scoring by using a sharp pencil along the edge of a ruler. The tabs should be glued then stuck in position.

Net of a hexagonal prism

You are going to make a model of a building. Below there is the net of a hexagonal prism. You can make the hexagonal prism then use it as your building or as part of your building – it would be ideal as a tower on a castle or a church.

1. Cut out the net then score along the dotted lines.

2. Fold it to make it into a hexagonal prism.

3. Glue the tabs then press them firmly into place.

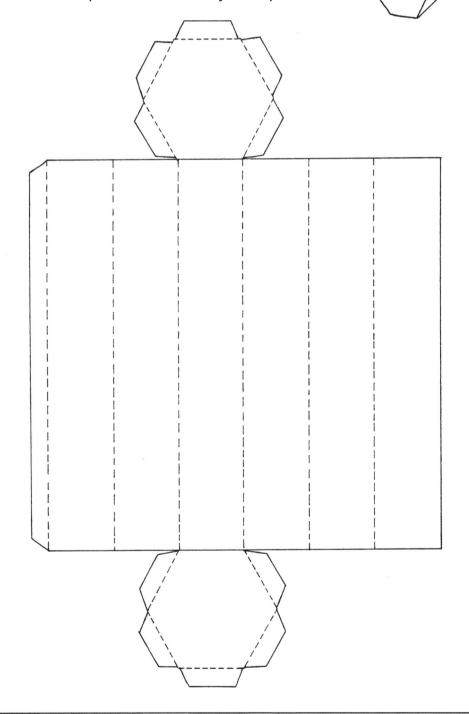

Teachers' notes Photocopy several copies of this net onto thin card. Encourage the children to cut it out very accurately and to take care when scoring by using a sharp pencil along the edge of a ruler. The tabs should be glued then stuck in position.

buildings	bungalow	castle
centre	church	cinema
college	cube	cuboid
cylinder	data	decide
decision	dwellings	employment
factory	frequency	hexagonal
historic	historical	history

Andrew Brodie: Geography Today 8–9 © A & C Black 2008

leisure	model	mosque
museum	offices	prism
pyramid	recreation	restaurant
school	score	settlement
sports	swimming	temple
theatre	triangular	types
windmill	wind turbine	worship

MAPS

Contents

This unit focuses on recognising the continents. It would be helpful if the pupils could have access to a world atlas while discussing the presentation. Three outline maps (Resource sheets 1–3) are provided. There are no worksheets in this unit.

This unit features:
- CD-ROM: MAPS 1–8
- Resource sheets 1–3

Useful resources

- Atlas of the World
- Globe

Learning objectives

- asking geographical questions
- using appropriate geographical vocabulary
- using maps and plans at a range of scales
- using secondary sources of information
- drawing maps and plans at a range of scales
- identifying and describing what places are like

- locating and describing where places are
- recognising how places fit within a wider geographical context
- recognising physical and human features in the environment

Resource sheets

Resource sheet 1: Map of the British Isles
Resource sheet 2: Map of Europe
Resource sheet 3: Map of the world

The CD-ROM

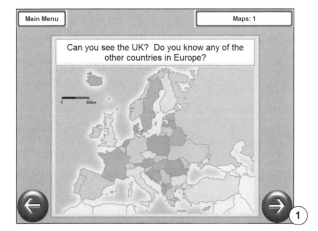

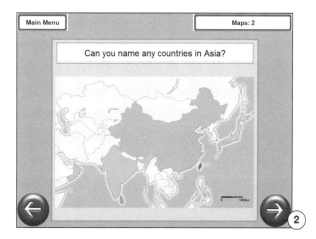

Explain that this is a map of a continent and that a continent is a large area of land. It usually made up of lots of countries. Ask the pupils if they know which continent it is. Can they name any countries in this continent? Can they name another continent that is joined to Europe? The pupils could also have access to a world atlas while discussing the presentation. Encourage them to refer to it to find answers to the questions. This is an interactive map. When touched country names will appear.

Ask the pupils to describe what a continent is and if they can identify which continent this is. Can they name any countries in this continent? Can they name another continent that is joined to Asia? This is an interactive map. When touched country names will appear.

The CD-ROM continued

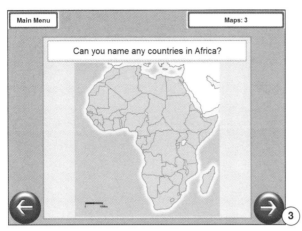

Ask the pupils to describe what a continent is and if they can identify which continent this is. Can they name any countries in this continent? What continent is directly to the north of Africa? What continent is to the north-east of Africa? What ocean is to the west of Africa? What ocean is to the east of Africa? When touched country names will appear.

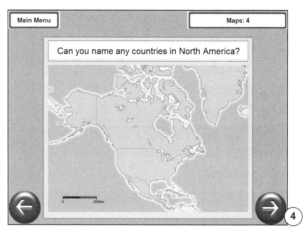

Ask the pupils to describe what a continent is and if they can identify which continent this is. Can they name any countries in this continent? What continent is directly to the south of North America? What ocean is to the west of North America? What ocean is to the east of North America? When touched country names will appear.

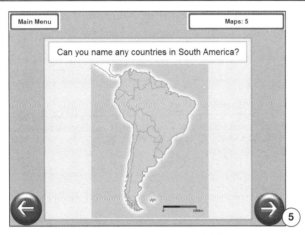

Ask the pupils to describe what a continent is and if they can identify which continent this is. Can they name any countries in this continent? What continent is directly to the north of South America? What ocean is to the west of South America? What ocean is to the east of South America? When touched country names will appear.

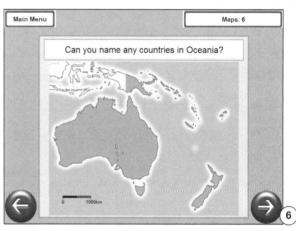

Explain that Oceania is an unusual continent because it includes lots of islands as well as one big land area. Ask the pupils what the big land area is called. When touched country names will appear.

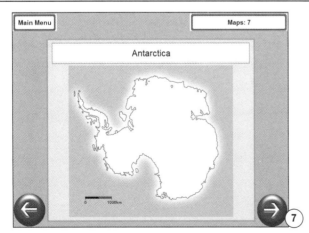

Ask the pupils to describe what a continent is and if they can identify which continent this is. What is different about it to the other continents we have seen? Explain that Antarctica doesn't have any countries. It is very cold and the only people living there are scientists who carry out investigations there. When touched country names and oceans will appear.

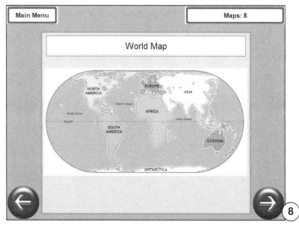

Explain to the pupils that the map shows all the continents. Point out that Antarctica appears like a ribbon along the bottom of the map because the map is a flat representation of a sphere – compare the map to a globe, pointing out Antarctica on both. Can the children identify each of the continents and the major oceans? When touched continents names and oceans will appear.

Map of the British Isles

British Isles

SCOTLAND

Edinburgh•

NORTHERN
IRELAND
Belfast•

ENGLAND

WALES

Cardiff•

London•

0   100km

Teachers' notes This map is very useful for any occasion when you need a clear map of the British Isles.

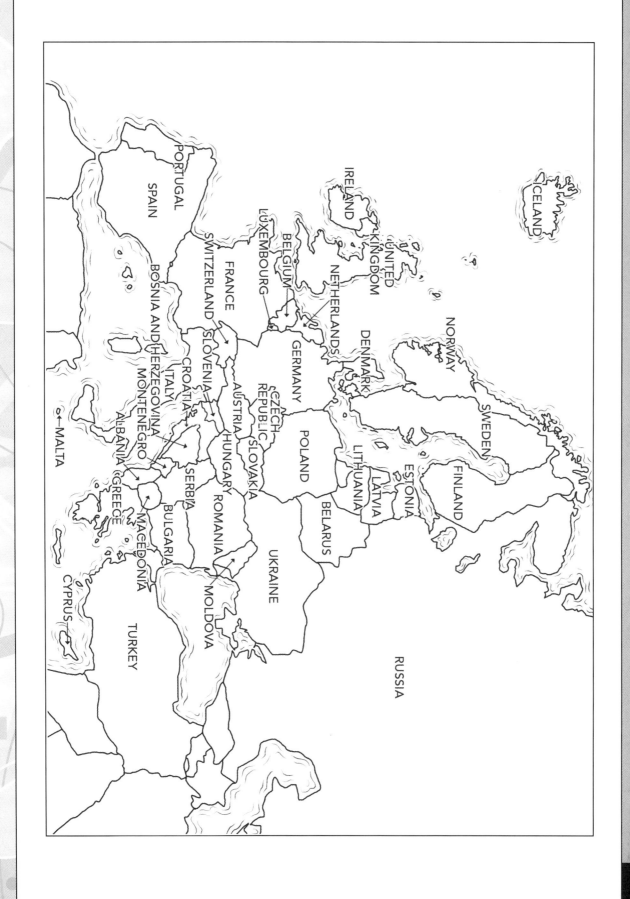

Teachers' notes This map is very useful for any occasion on when you need a clear map of Europe.

Map of the World

OCEANIA

ASIA

EUROPE

AFRICA

ANTARCTICA

Indian Ocean

Atlantic Ocean

NORTH
AMERICA

SOUTH
AMERICA

Pacific Ocean

Equator

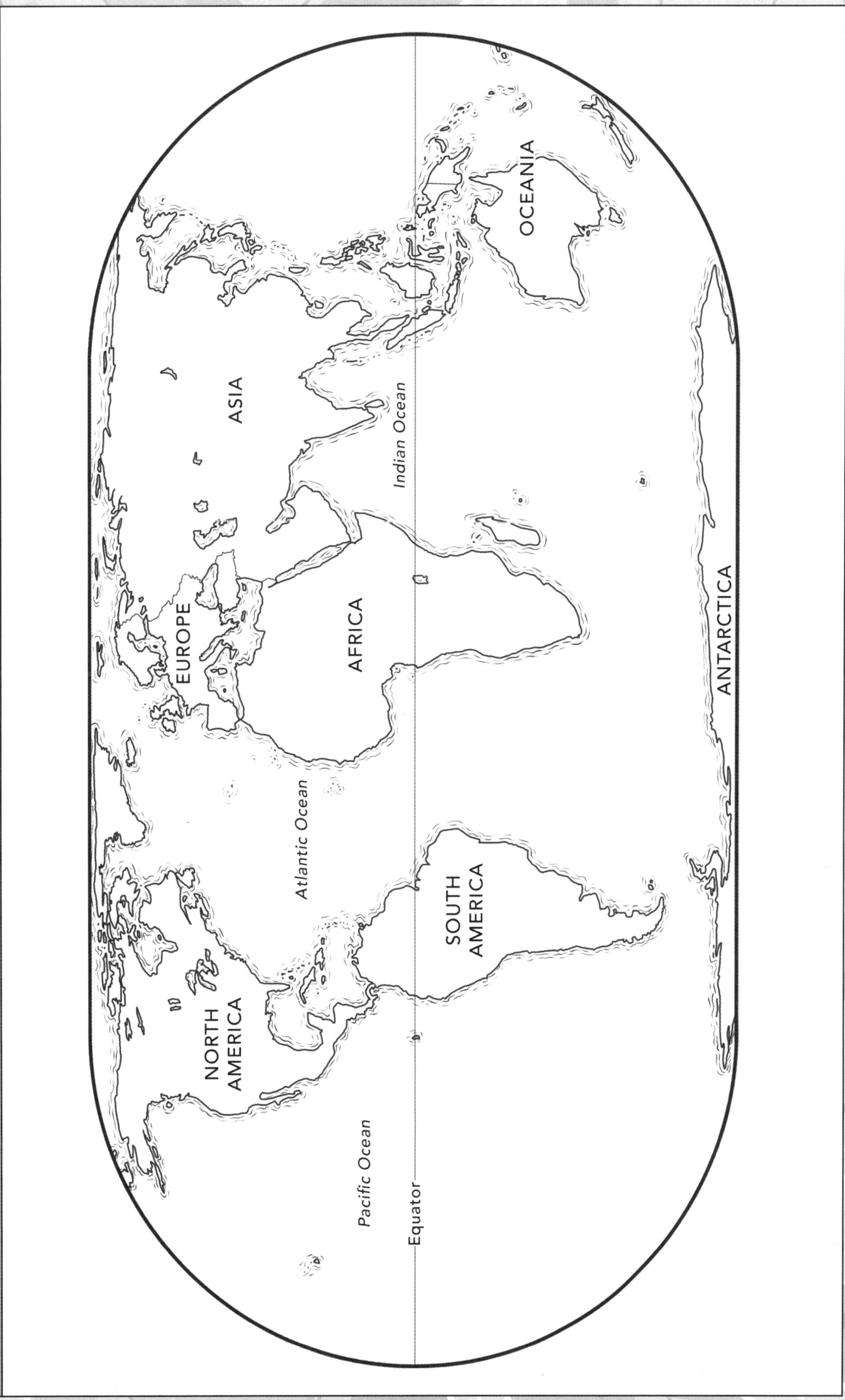

Teachers' notes   This map is very useful for any occasion when you need a clear map of the World.

Andrew Brodie: Geography Today 8–9 © A & C Black 2008

Africa	**America**	**Antarctica**
Arctic	**Asia**	**Atlantic**
Australia	**British Isles**	**Europe**
Great Britain	**Indian**	**Ireland**
Mediterranean	**North**	**Oceania**
Pacific	**South**	**Southern**
United Kingdom	**World**	

Andrew Brodie: Geography Today 8–9 © A & C Black 2008